Priority Publications Delhi

priority PUBLICATIONS

Language Skills

Early Writing

Shab

This book belongs to

Name : ______________________

Class : ______________________

School : ______________________

Priority Publications

Published by Priority Publications
7/7, Ansari Road, Daryaganj
New Delhi 110002, INDIA
+91 11 4156 3757
info@dspublishers.com
www.dspublishers.com

ISBN 978-81-8022-109-5

First published in 2010
Reprint 2022

10 9 8 7 6 5 4

Printed in India

₹ 175

PREFACE

Children of the ages between 3 years and 5 years are at the Pre-Primary stage of learning, and just about awakened to their sensory skills.

This series of books is basically revolving round children of these ages and are thus directed towards the development of the skills to which the tiny beings are getting introduced to. They are being initiated into the concepts that are necessary for further progress of the learning procedures.

This set of books deals separately with specific language skills. With these books at hand, followed by the guidance of the teacher or parents will take the children ahead in fixing in their minds the correct concepts necessary for further education.

The activities enshrined in these books help the child in developing his/her basic skills of reading and writing.

Top to Bottom, Straight Strokes

Motor Skill

Join the dots.

Teacher/Parents Help the child to draw from top to bottom for preparation of letters f, i, l, t, j.

Motor Skill

Top to Bottom, Vertical Straight Back Strokes

Join the dots and complete the bricks to form a castle.

Teacher/Parents Direct the child to draw from top to bottom for vertical strokes.

Top to Bottom, Eye-Hand Co-ordination

Draw and complete the raindrops falling.

Motor Skill

Formation of Straight Backs

Trace and complete the patterns.

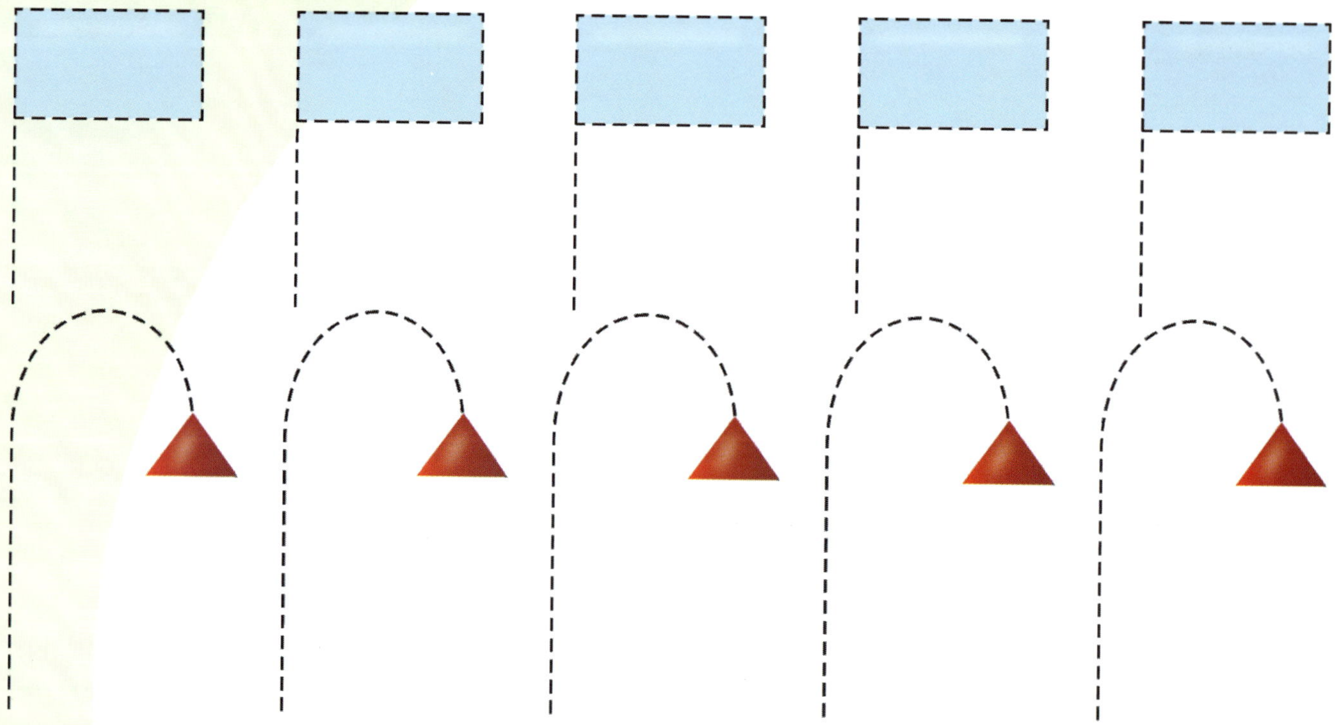

Draw the fishing hooks.

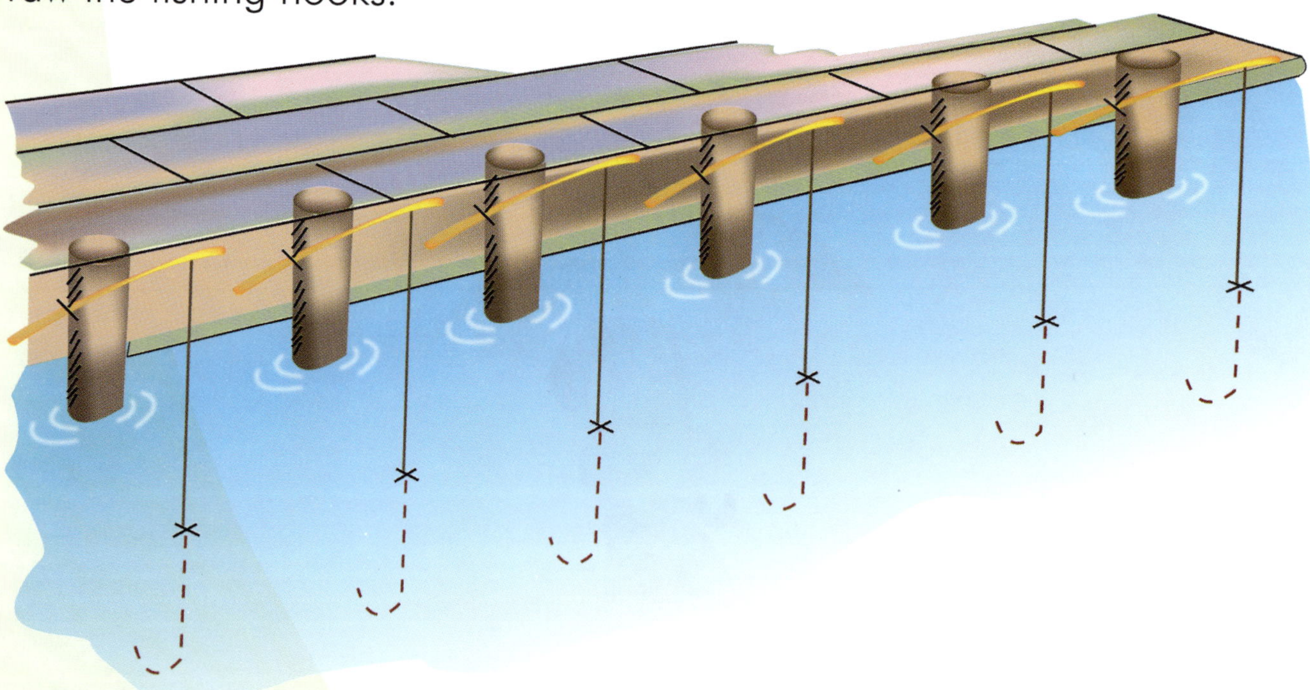

Teacher/Parents

Make sure that the child begins letters f and t with the vertical stroke before adding short horizontal line.

Formation of Straight Back Letters

Writing Skill

Trace and copy the letters and word.

f f f f

l l l l

t t t t

i i i i

j j j j

jill jill

Motor Skill

Formation of Semi-circular Strokes

Trace the ducks.

Trace the caterpillars.

Teacher/Parents Direct the child to form the letter 'c' in an anti-clockwise stroke, from top to bottom.

Formation of Circular Lines

Motor Skill

Trace the circles with coloured pencils.

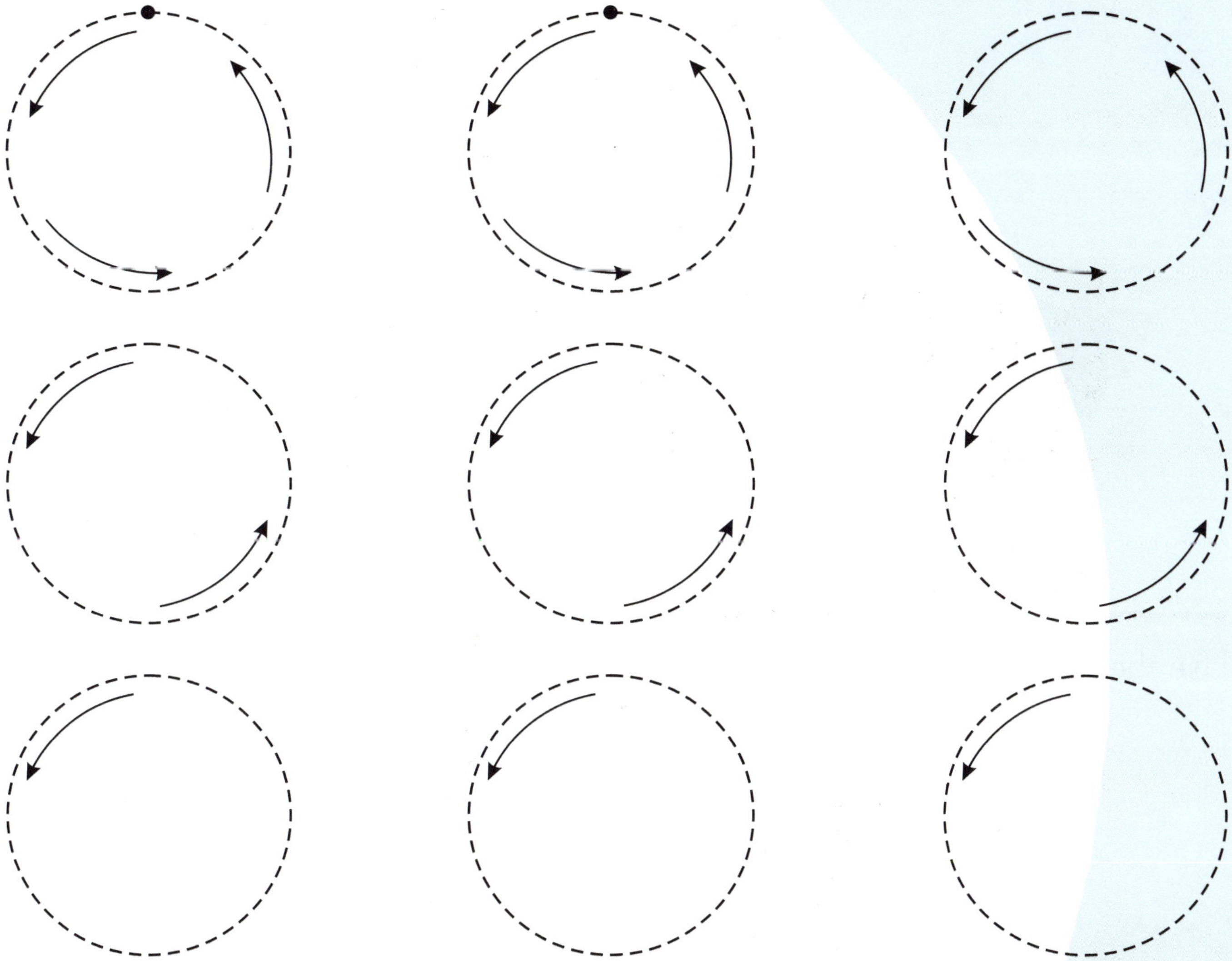

Teacher/Parents Ensure that the child forms circles in anti-clockwise direction for formation of a, c, d, o, q.

Motor Skill

Circular Strokes

Trace the bubbles.

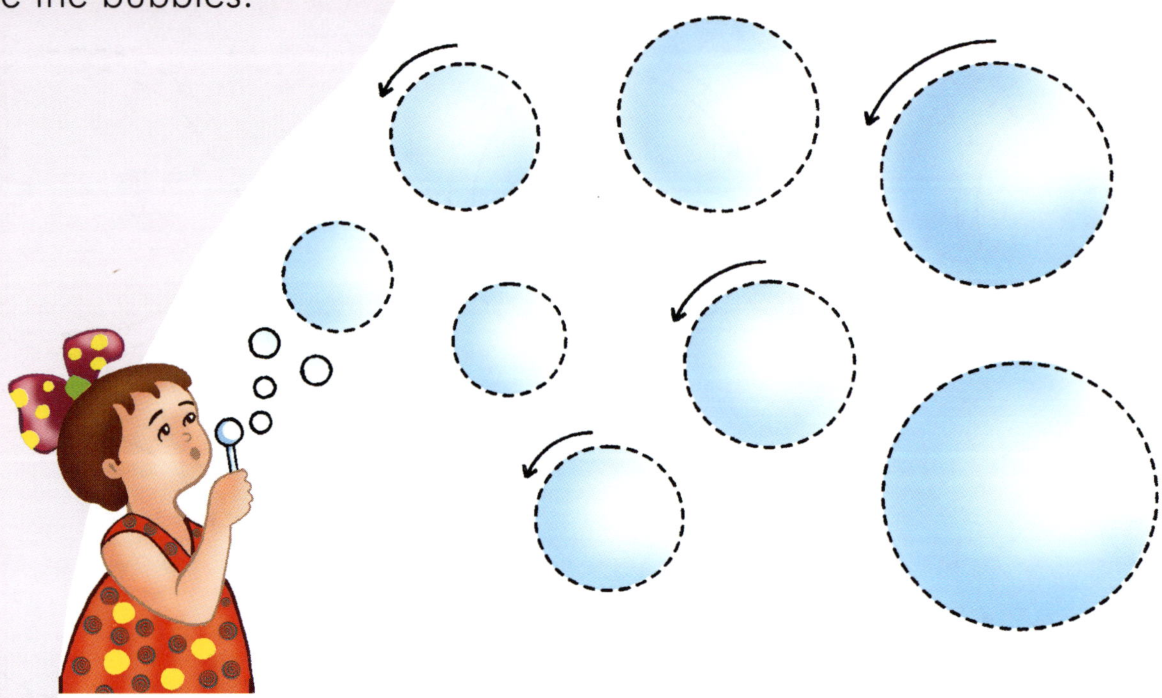

Use the coloured pencil to trace and draw snails.

Teacher/Parents Help the child to begin the stroke in an anti-clockwise direction.

Formation of Circular Loops

Motor Skill

Help the bumble-bees find their path.

Motor Skill

More Practice on Circular Strokes

Trace and complete the patterns.

Pattern Drawing for Letters 'c', 'e'

Motor Skill

Trace and complete the following patterns.

Writing Skill

Correct Formation of Letters a, c, e, o, g, q

Trace the letters.

a a a a a a a a

c c c c c c c c

e e e e e e e e

o o o o o o o o

g g g g g g g g

q q q q q q q q

Teacher/Parents Help the child to read and recognise the letters.

Oblique Strokes

Trace the dots to match the pictures.

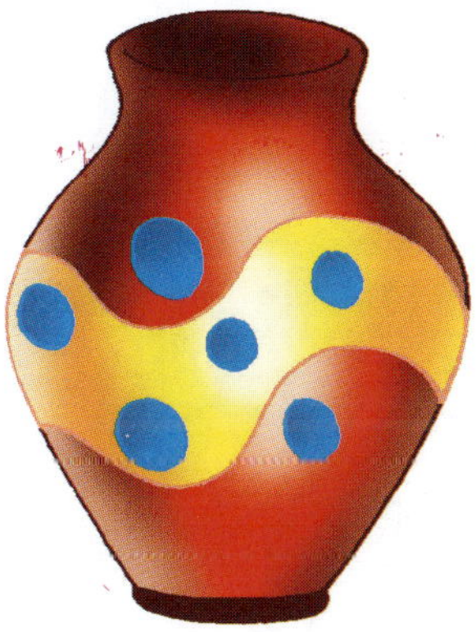

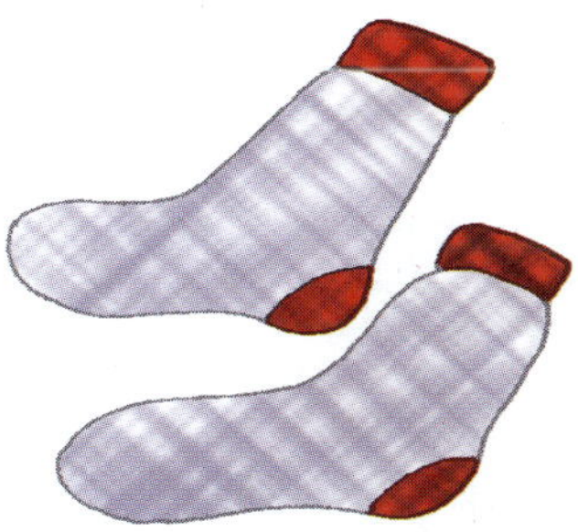

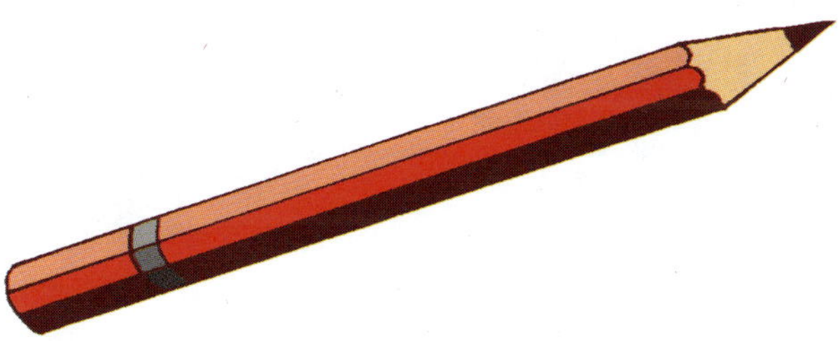
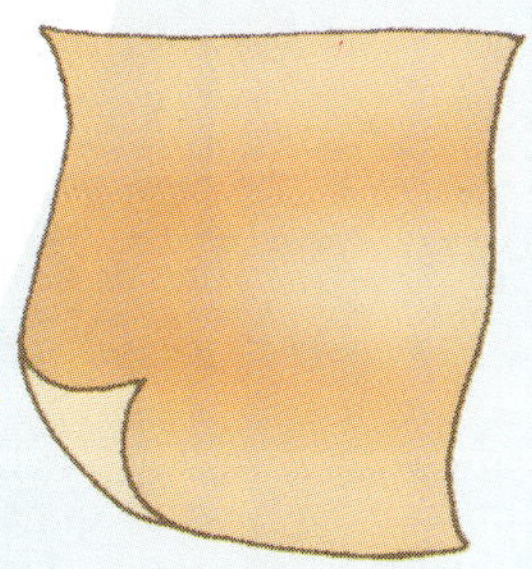

Teacher/Parents — Discuss the pictures with the child. Allow more practice of oblique strokes for writing letters v, w, x, y, z

Formation of Oblique Strokes

Trace the missing parts of the pictures.

Correct Formation of Letters v, w, x

Writing Skill

Trace the patterns and letters.

Writing Skill

Correct Formation of Letters v, w, x, y, z

Trace the letters.

v v v v v v v v

w w w w w w w w

x x x x x x x x

y y y y y y y y

z z z z z z z z

x y z x y z x y z x y z

Formation of Overswing Patterns

Help the rabbit, lamb and deer find their way home.

Teacher/Parents Overswing strokes for formation of letters h, n, m.

Motor Skill

Formation of Overswings

Trace the path of the honey-bee.

Trace the igloos.

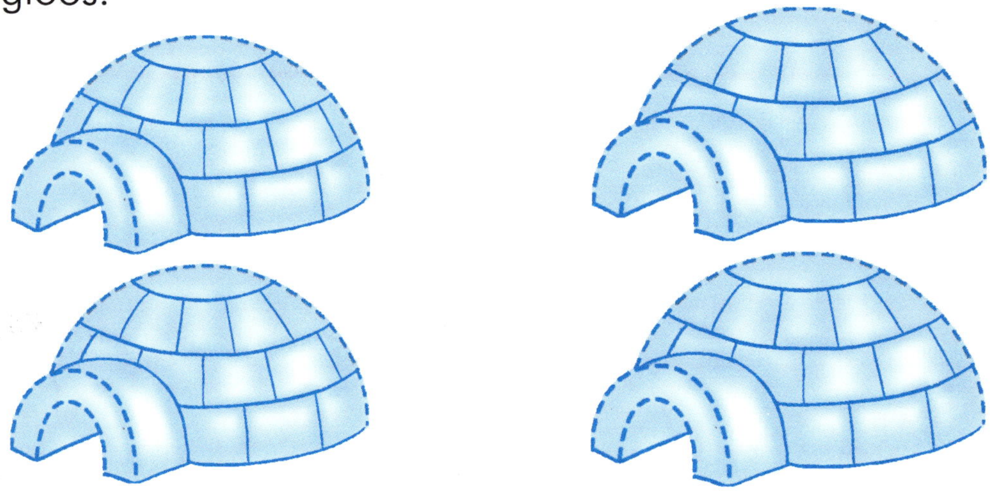

Trace and draw the sand-castles.

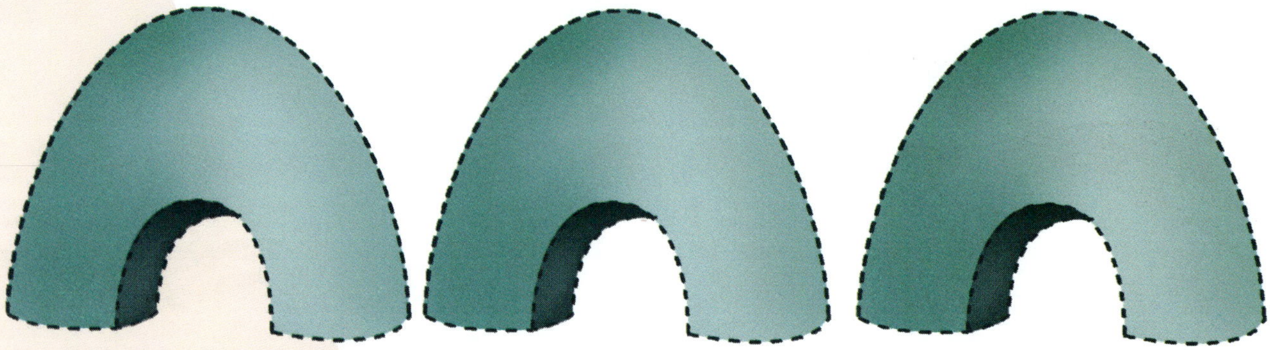

Correct Formation of h, m, n, r

Writing Skill

Trace the letters and patterns.

Writing Skill

Formation of Letters h, m, n, r

Trace and copy the pattern, letters and words.

mmmmmmmmmmmmmmmmmmmmm

hmn mnr hmr rhn

man hen ran

Teacher/Parents Check that the child begins letters h, m, n, r with the top-down stroke.

Underswing Strokes

Trace the patterns.

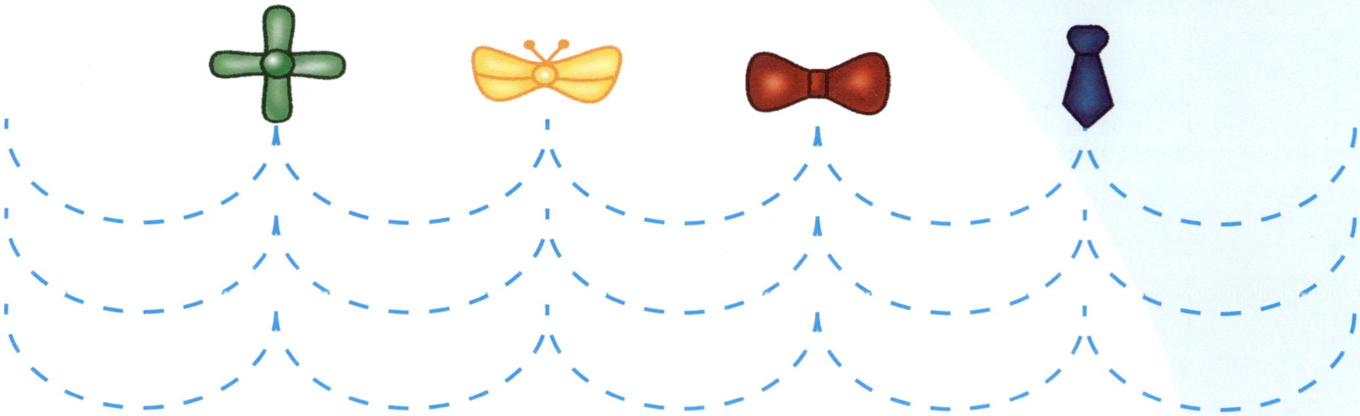

Trace the dots to complete the picture.

Motor Skill

Overswing and Underswing Strokes

Use coloured pencils to trace the patterns.

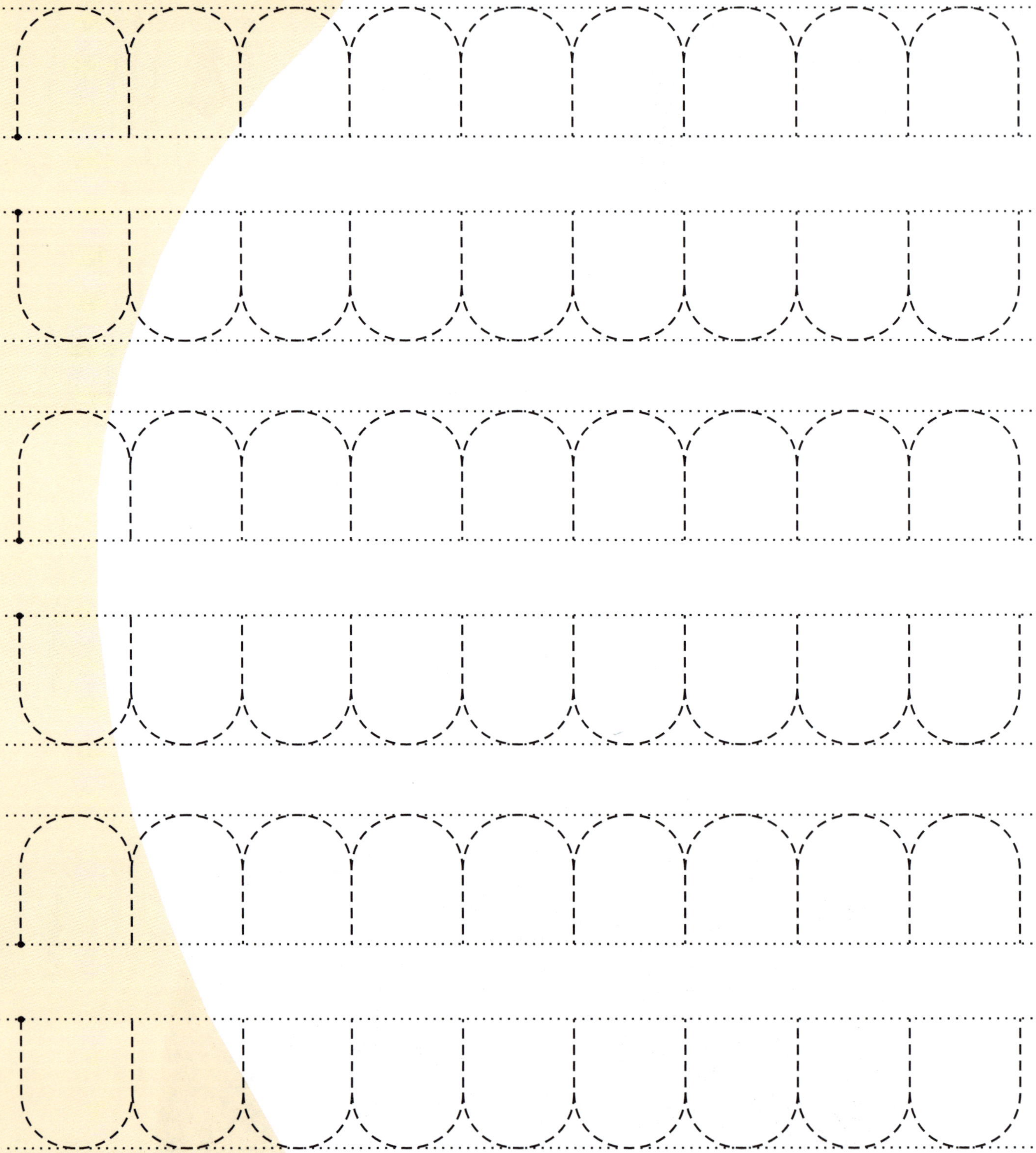

Formation of Letter u

Writing Skill

Trace the pattern and the letter u.

Writing Skill

Formation of Letters u, m, n

Trace and copy the letters and words.

u u u u u u

uu uu uu uu uu

run mum nun

Overswing Strokes for Letters b, p

Motor Skill

Trace the path of the bumblebee.

Teacher/Parents

Encourage the child to form overswing pattern (clockwise) for letters b and p.

Motor Skill

Formation of Overswing Letters b, p

Trace the pattern and then letter.

b b b b b b

p p p p p p

bpb bpb bpb

Teacher/Parents — More practice for formation of letters b,p

Correct Formation of Letters b, p

Writing Skill

Trace and copy the letters.

b p b p b p

bbb ppp ppp bbb

pbp pbp pbp pbp

Motor Skill

Eye-hand Co-ordination for Letter s

Draw lines to show the path of cars coming down the hills.

Teacher/Parents Encourage the child to form the pattern with anti-clockwise strokes for the letter s.

Formation of Semi-circular Lines for Letter s

Trace the lines to draw snakes on snakes and ladders. Colour the picture as of your own choice.

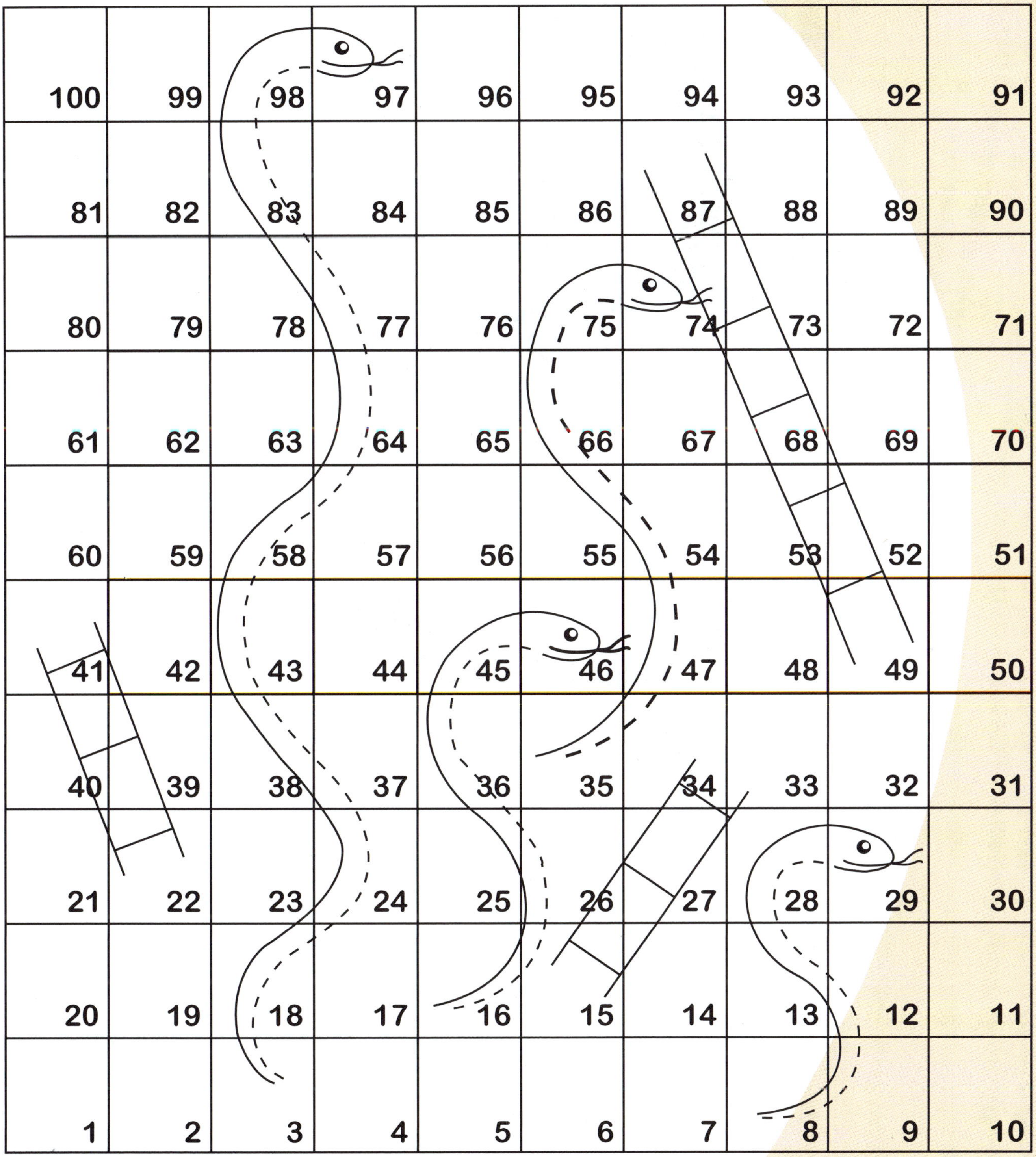

Teacher/Parents More practice of semi-circular strokes for formation of letter s.

Writing Skill

Formation of Letter s

Trace and write the letter s.

s s s s s s

s

Words with Straight Back Letters i, l, t

Writing Skill

Trace the sentence.

Ten little turtles

walking down a

hill.

Teacher/Parents Encourage the child to space out the words evenly.

Writing Skill

Writing Words with i, l, t, f

Trace and copy the sentences.

Left - right - left.

The soldiers walk

on foot.

Writing Skill

Words with Circular Letters

Trace and copy the sentences.

Look at the cows

and the goats.

Cows eat grass.

Goats eat grass.

Writing Skill

Words with Letters c and e

Trace and copy the sentences.

I have a cock and
a hen. My pets
cock and hen like
bread and corn.

Writing Skill

Words with Letters k, d, q

Trace and copy the sentence.

The king and the queen had a kind daughter.

Writing Skill

Words with Oblique Letters v, w, y

Trace and copy the sentence.

Wendy and Vicky

have a yo-yo

and a toy van.

Writing Skill

Writing Words with Letters x, z

Trace and copy the sentence.

Alexander likes to

see the zebra in

the zoo.

Writing Skill

Words with Letters m, n, r

Trace and copy the sentence.

Nine mice meet in

a small house to

have a nice dinner.

Writing Skill

Words with Letter u

Trace and copy the sentence.

Ruth is walking

under a purple

umbrella.

Writing Skill

Words with Letters b, p

Trace and copy the sentence.

Bobby has two

pet birds - a parrot

and a pigeon.

Writing Skill

Writing Words with Letter s

Trace and copy the sentence.

The sun rises in

the east and sets

in the west.

Writing Skill

Writing Words

Trace the sentences.

I am a big animal.

I have a long trunk.

I have big ears.